CW00401088

BRUNEL

a railtour of his achievements

Vic Mitchell

MP Middleton Press

Cover pictures: Memorials to Brunel include a working broad gauge locomotive Fire Fly, seen in the goods transfer shed at the Didcot Railway Centre (top): the majestic train shed at Paddington (lower and back).

FOREWORD

Isambard Kingdom Brunel (1806-1859) was the foremost engineer in an age of great engineers. His ability, courage and enthusiasm inspired his workforce constructing feats of engineering which surpassed all that had gone before.

Most notable among his achievements are the Maidenhead and Royal Albert Bridges, Sonning Cutting approximately 3km long by 18m deep through varying geology and Box Tunnel, which at 3km was the longest railway tunnel in the world at that time.

The distinctive style of Middleton Press takes the reader on six fascinating railtours of Brunel's crowning glory, the Great Western Railway, highlighting his milestone achievements and magnificent station structures. It is a fitting tribute to Brunel's genius that his Great Western Railway forms a vital and not inconsiderable part of Britain's transport infrastructure today.

Douglas Allenby, BSc(Hons), PhD, CEng, FICE, FGS,
Chief Tunnelling Engineer, Edmund Nuttall Limited.
January 2006

Published March 2006

ISBN 1 904474 74 8

© *Middleton Press, 2006*

Design Deborah Esher
Typesetting Barbara Mitchell

Published by
> *Middleton Press*
> *Easebourne Lane*
> *Midhurst, West Sussex*
> *GU29 9AZ*
Tel: 01730 813169
Fax: 01730 812601
Email: info@middletonpress.co.uk
www.middletonpress.co.uk

Printed & bound by Biddles Ltd, Kings Lynn

CONTENTS

ACKNOWLEDGEMENTS

The idea for this unique volume came from Dr. D.Allenby, Vice Chairman of ICE South which is responsible for organising a number of events in Portsmouth to commemorate the 200th Anniversary of the birth of Isambard Kingdom Brunel. I am grateful for this and for his foreword.

The majority of the illustrations, being of great antiquity, are deposited in various public collections. Private collections accessed include those of R.S.Carpenter, M.Dart, Lens of Sutton, Kidderminster Railway Museum, C.G.Maggs, D.H.Mitchell, M.J.Stretton and the Institution of Civil Engineers (ICE) whose chief librarian, Mr. M.Chrimes, has been extremely helpful. The photographers are shown where known and apologies are given for any omissions.

Valuable help has been received in the final stages of production from A.R.Carder, N.Langridge, Mr. D & Dr. S.Salter and particularly my dear wife, Barbara.

I am immensely grateful to all those mentioned above who have helped create this memorial in their own individual ways. Little did I know when I attended my first college in Acton that it would become part of Brunel University and that I would thus be able to claim two remote and tenuous links with such a great engineer and inspiration to us all. He did not have to suffer the excesses of the modern Institute of Objectors; let us work to create more great innovators in this fine country.

I.   This diagram indicates the main routes with which Brunel was involved and thus some of those on which his legacy can be seen today. Most of the principal stations are marked, as are those branches included in this volume. To aid location, the illustrations herein of the smaller stations are placed in journey order, except in the section on the branches.

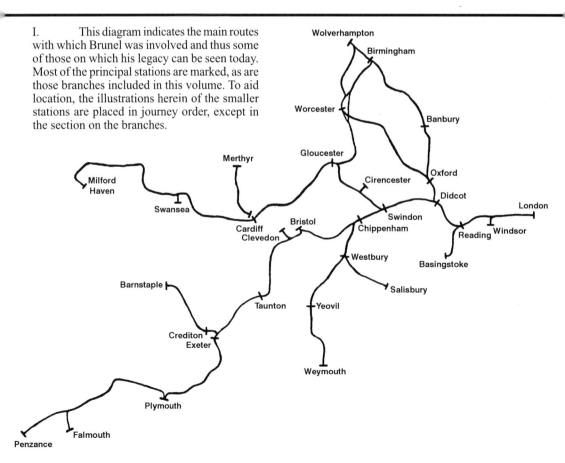

INDEX

INTRODUCTION

More than 50 books have appeared on Isambard Kingdom Brunel, technical and biographical, or both. This is the first album to look solely at his railway legacy, although many of the views are of structures now lost. They are in journey order from London and include many familiar panoramas, together with less well known locations, where work was carried out in Brunel's style by his subordinates, occasionally posthumously.

The first section gives a brief background and readers are strongly recommended to read one of the biographies, once they have been impressed by the man's achievements after seeing this volume.

No claim is made that a comprehensive collection of contemporary views is included in this book. Many of Brunel's smaller bridges are omitted, as are a number of tunnel portals and stone retaining walls, many of which are in the Bath area.

Some railways are omitted for which Brunel was engineer as no visual records have been obtained, but the feature of his lines for which he will be best remembered was the broad gauge track. This was laid at an amazing 7ft 0¼ins between rails, but it prevented through running to the rest of Britain. It is extensively illustrated herein, as is the prolonged conversion process to 4ft 8½ins.

He is also widely known for the atmospheric railway, although it was not his idea. He specified it for the South Devon Railway, as it avoided the use of locomotives in this hilly terrain. It was a spectacular failure; please see pictures 3.14 to 3.24 for details.

EARLY DAYS

Isambard Kingdom Brunel was born in Portsea, Portsmouth, on 9th April 1806. His father, Marc Brunel, had emigrated from France during the Revolution and had proved to be a talented engineer. He married Sophia Kingdom and they settled in a small house, close to Portsmouth Naval Dockyard.

It was here that he had his first major engineering success, in the form of a production line series of machines for the manufacture of pulley blocks. He also educated his son in his early years and guided him into an engineering career.

Marc Brunel was appointed engineer for the first tunnel under the River Thames, in July 1825. He was taken ill in April 1826 and his son took over, despite his inexperience in this field. Catastrophic flooding in January 1828 brought work to a halt and it was not resumed until 1836. The tunnel was completed in 1843 and Marc Brunel received a knighthood, his death following in 1849.

In the meantime, the young Brunel had started design work on two suspension bridges: Hungerford over the River Thames and Clifton over the River Avon. The latter was severely delayed due to procrastination over a design competition. Brunel eventually won.

Not only was his engineering practice involved with bridges, but consultation and survey work was in progress on an increasing number of railways, notably the Great Western Railway (GWR). It is on these that this album concentrates, but one of Brunel's ships is included herein, as he regarded it as simply an extension of the GWR by effectively providing a ferry service to the USA.

Brunel was involved in the construction of about 1200 miles of railway in Britain and so this volume is necessarily a superficial representation of the subject, but it is intended to convey an impression of the achievements in the railway world of this undoubted Great Briton. He was voted second in TV's Greatest Briton contest in 2003 (Sir Winston Churchill was first), but he would be rated, no doubt, as the Greatest Engineer in any competition. In the view of a recent biographer, he embraced 18 modern professions.

FURTHER ILLUSTRATIONS

Other views of stations and structures seen herein can be found in various Middleton Press albums and for easy reference the ISBN suffix is shown at the end of the first caption at each location. The series title and the book titles can be established from the table below; they are listed in order of publication.

ISBN Prefix   A = 0 906520, B = 1 873793, C = 1 901706, D = 1 904474

1. BACKGROUND

←————

1.1   The twin bore Thames Tunnel was intended to reduce London's traffic congestion, but its builders were never able to fund the spiral approach roads. Thus it was a financial disaster and was only ever used by pedestrians and a street market. The Brunel Engine House at Rotherhithe was converted into a museum of that name. B804

←————

1.2   A new use was found for the Thames Tunnel in 1865 when the East London Railway began using it; it is now part of the Underground network. The northern portals at Wapping are visible still, but the stench for which the tunnel was infamous came to an end in 1995 when it was at last made waterproof. (A.C.Mott)

1.3   Hungerford Bridge was built for pedestrians and barrows to reach Hungerford Market, at the west end of the Strand. In the background is the famous shot tower which stood close to Waterloo station until the 1950s. The bridge opened in 1845, but was dismantled in 1862 to make way for a railway bridge to Charing Cross. This still uses Brunel's brick piers. A754

1.4   Work began on the Clifton Suspension Bridge in June 1831, but delays ensued beyond Brunel's control. However, an iron bar was eventually fixed between the towers and the foolhardy were able to travel across the Avon Gorge in a basket, a rope hauling them from the mid-point.   D187

1.5   The Clifton Bridge was a lifelong frustration for Brunel and a group within the Institution of Civil Engineers made arrangements for it to be completed after his death, as a memorial to him. Originally intended only for pedestrians, it was redesigned for the road traffic of the day and to allow use of the redundant chains from Hungerford Bridge. The design had been altered so much that the Brunel family refused to attend its opening in December 1864. The 1867 Portishead branch is near the floor of the valley in this early 20th century view.

2. London to Bristol

2.1   The first station at Paddington was west of the present structure and lasted sixteen years. Much of the passenger accommodation was in the arches under Bishop's Road - right. These would eventually take trains into the majestic new station.   C370, C818

2.2   The initial terminus was extremely cramped, but Brunel intended it to be temporary. It would be transposed with the goods depot in 1854 and the engine shed would eventually be further west.

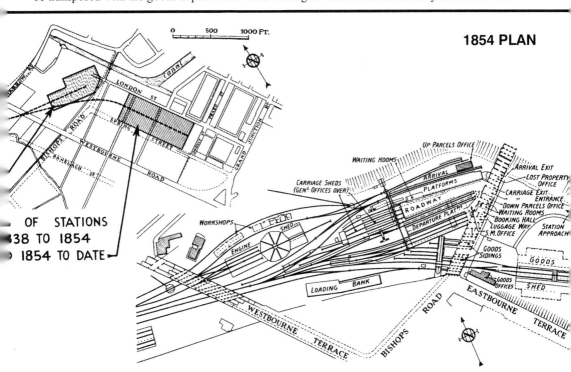

1854 PLAN

2.3   The cathedral scale of the new terminus received wide acclaim, its design being attributed in part to Brunel's architect, Matthew Digby Wyatt. The Great Western Hotel was soon opened in the background.

2.4   The 1854 layout included only four platforms, but many wagon turntables, as well as larger ones for the transfer of locomotives. Many private carriages of the gentry were conveyed on flat wagons and were manhandled to and from the loading docks.

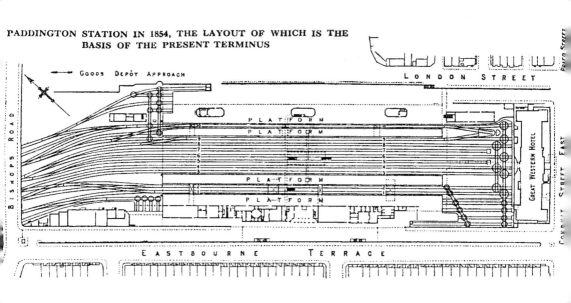

PADDINGTON STATION IN 1854, THE LAYOUT OF WHICH IS THE BASIS OF THE PRESENT TERMINUS

2.5   A splendid feature of the transept was a balcony, seen on the left. Below it are Queen Victoria's private rooms. Evident here, in the foreground, are traversers, which had replaced the turntables specified by Brunel. The last broad gauge train had left on 20th May 1892.

2.6   At the north end of Bishop's Road was a bridge over the canal leading to Paddington Basin. It had been designed by Brunel so that its cast iron components were in compression. It is being dismantled after discovery in 2003; parts have been preserved. (NCE)

2.7　　　One of the finest memorials to Brunel is the great train shed at Paddington, seen from platform 1 on 28th September 2005, the date of the following two pictures. The entire structure had been extensively renovated in the preceding years. (Author)

2.8　　　The Great Western Hotel is behind the splendid screen at the east end of the south shed. The circulating area has always been known as "The Lawn". In Brunel's day, this meant a piece of waste ground, such as the untillable corners of a field. (Author)

2.9   The statue of I.K.Brunel was completed in 1982 by John Doubleday and was initially positioned at a busy location at the top of the escalators to the Underground. It was moved to face platform 1, thus being passed by those arriving by taxi. (Author)

2.10   With the benefit of hindsight, it became clear that Brunel made an error of judgement at the first junction west of London, when he allowed the 1844 West London Railway to cross on the level. A crossbar signal, plus a turnpike pole for added safety, are halting a train from Willesden Junction, while an express from the West of England approaches. Sadly the drawing is one rail short under Scrubs Lane bridge, which is shown on the map.   B847, C370

2.11   The location of Old Oak Common East Junction is lower left on this 1867 map scaled at 6ins to 1 mile and the GWR is the lower one to cross the page. The West London Line ran over the main line on a bridge from 1860 onwards. The Brunel family grave is in the cemetery on the right.

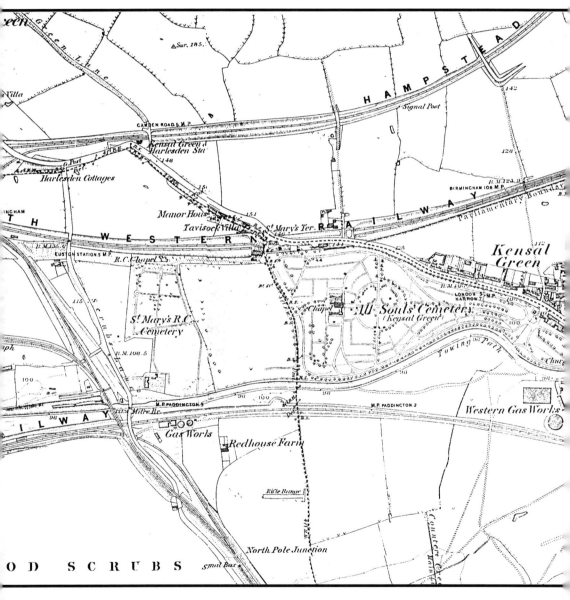

2.12 Some engravings give accurate records of the original broad gauge configuration of longitudinal timber separated by transoms. This is an impression of Ealing station when still surrounded by fields and orchards.   C370, C427

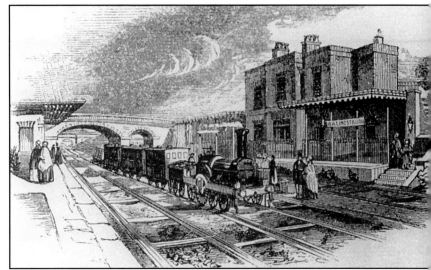

2.13 Included to show broad gauge stock, this photo was taken about 30 years after Brunel's death. However, the coaches have normal bodies for remounting after gauge conversion. The "Iron Duke" 4-2-2 is running west through Castle Hill & Ealing Dean, known as West Ealing since 1899.   C427, C508

2.14 Minimal provisions for passengers were made at Hanwell, where the station was built on an embankment. It is now served exclusively by Heathrow Connect trains from Paddington. It is well worthwhile taking one here and walking through the park to enjoy Wharncliffe Viaduct.   C427

2.15   The viaduct was necessary to cross the valley of the River Brent, which is shown on the left, flowing towards Brentford. This is another important memorial to Brunel's grand designs. Given more powerful locomotives, an embankment may have sufficed.

2.16   The north side and the approaching river was recorded before the structure was widened on this elevation to take two more tracks. Sadly, uncontrolled tree growth has largely spoilt this view.

2.17   The narrower additional plinth for the widening was evident in 2005, as was Lord Wharncliffe's coat of arms. Queen Victoria was reputed to have once had her Windsor-bound train stop here, so that she could enjoy the view of Middlesex. (Author)

2.18   Scattered below the viaduct in 2005 were pieces of bridge rail from Brunel's era. They appear to have been bent for later use in fencing. (Author)

2.19   The modest structures at Southall lasted until the quadrupling of this section in 1877-79. This is the up side building before the opening of the Brentford branch in the year of Brunel's death. C427, C508

2.20   Pressure from Eton College meant that a station at Slough could not be provided initially. However, Slough was listed in the first timetable, but no mention was made of the lack of platforms. When this station was completed both platforms were in line, a system employed at other principal stations. They were on the town side.   C427, C567, C77X

2.21   The west elevation of Slough station is on the left, as is one of the wagons mentioned in caption 2.4. On the right is the Royal Hotel; no doubt its appearance regularly impressed royalty until the opening of the Windsor branch from here in 1849.

2.22   The initial service was described as "to Maidenhead", but the station was remote from the town, east of the River Thames. However, it was close to the Bath Road for connecton with traditional transport. This seems an elaborate structure for a temporary terminus.   C567

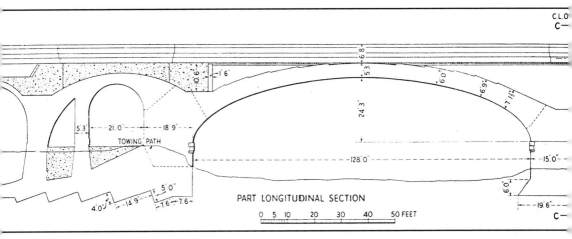

PART LONGITUDINAL SECTION

0   5 10   20   30   40   50 FEET

2.23   Brunel's bold bridge design is exemplified at Maidenhead with his almost flat brick arch concept. The main span and one arch have been taken from one of his drawings. It was the flattest arch in the world at that time. Critics said that it would collapse!   C567

2.24   The revolutionary style was a development of Telford's stone design and is seen under construction. The wooden shuttering of the two main spans over the Thames was lowered only slightly after the bricklaying was complete, in case Brunel's critics were right.

2.25   Maidenhead bridge had stood the test of time and still stands as a reminder of its designer's genius. It was later widened on both sides and so a deck chair on a boat is the ideal way to examine the original. The bridge for the Bath Road makes a notable comparison in the background.

2.26   Twyford had temporary buildings initially and these are seen in about 1845. The loop on the left was presumably in anticipation of the opening of the Henley branch in 1857. All was lost prior to the 1893 quadrupling.   C567

2.27   Sonning Cutting, on the approach to Reading, was the next major civil engineering task for Brunel, after the embankments at Hanwell. Again, it could have been less so had greater locomotive power been available. The Bath Road was given brick arches, but timber sufficed for a local lane. It was a prototype for more to follow in Devon and Cornwall.

2.28   As at Slough, the main stations had one sided platforms. Up trains used the east end at Reading, as seen here in about 1852 after an extra platform had been added. Down trains used the west end and the centre part was used for parcels and other light goods.   A479, C567, C796

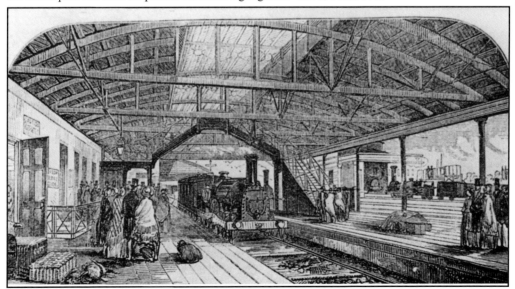

2.29   The Brunelian roof lasted into the photographic era, but the second platform did not. The building on the right was completed in 1868 and survives today. The photograph was taken between 1892 and 1896.

2.30   Pangbourne was typical of the smaller stations with its chalet-style building widely employed by Brunel. One of his less durable ideas was steps in the platform edge. His route through the Chiltern Hills could not be improved upon and remains the only one to be almost level.   C796

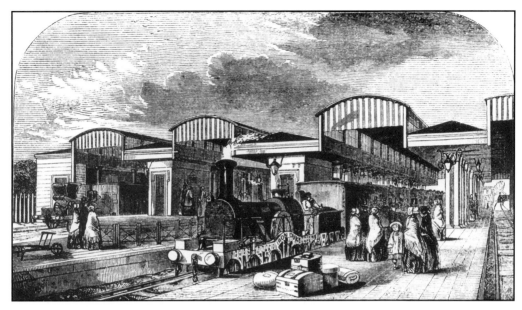

2.31　　　Brunel had more experience of station design by the time one was required as a junction for Oxford at Didcot. Opened in 1844, the nearby village was known as Dudcote. The next station west was Steventon and GWR board meetings were held at this half-way point on many occasions.　C133, C796, C842, D020

2.32　　　Swindon was chosen as the mid-way location for operational and passenger refreshment purposes. Substantial buildings were erected on both sides of the tracks and the station became a junction in 1841, initially for Cirencester and later for South Wales. The train in the centre is bound for Paddington. C842, C966, D306, D462

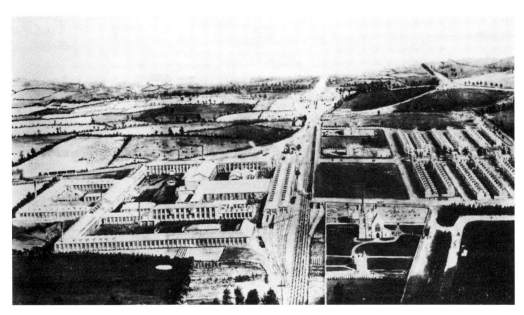

2.33   The main works of the GWR (left) was built at Swindon as was a new town (right) for workers and staff. Even Brunel was unlikely to imagine that they would peak at over 12,000 men. The line to Bristol is in the foreground, while the South Wales route curves to the left.

2.34   This westward view from the station features the works, which opened in 1843 and Brunel's intention was that it should provide all engineering services of a mechanical nature for the GWR. The South Wales trains took the curve to the right.

2.35   The rural site was well chosen, as it allowed for expansion; the carriage works is in the right background of another view from about 1890. The end of the broad gauge was nigh; it was never laid on the right. Other views can be found in pictures 5.1 and 5.2.

2.36   Both buildings from the Brunel era could be seen clearly for a brief period around 1970, after the demolition of the carriage shed that had stood in the foreground and before the demolition of the original down side structure, right. Thankfully the other can still be enjoyed.

2.37   Chippenham was provided with two platforms; a London-bound train stands at the up one. The building on the left is still used by passengers, although there is no track at the adjacent platform now.   C966, D128

2.38   The bridge west of Chippenham station can be considered to be Brunel's finest masonry road bridge. After abandonment of the broad gauge, it carried three standard gauge tracks, the centre one being a reversing siding.

2.39   The structure was completed in 1841 and widened in 1848. It is now at the junction of the A4 with the A429 and a zebra has replaced the sheep in this southward view from 2002. (C.G.Maggs)

2.40   The construction of Box Tunnel was one of Brunel's greatest challenges on the route and his east portal is shown to have been reduced in height. This was done in about 1900. The arch on the right gave access to limestone mines.   C966

2.41   Box Tunnel was largely unlined at its eastern end, but after broad gauge operation ceased, there was plenty of space in which to add a brick lining. The excavated Bath stone was used for building work on other parts of the route. The tunnel was almost two miles long and around 100 men lost their lives during the five-year construction period.

2.42   The west portal and its complex stonework was recorded with a disc and crossbar signal soon after opening. The rising sun is reputed to penetrate the tunnel briefly on Brunel's birthday; it does so three days earlier, on 6th April, according to one expert, but another gives varying dates and once only every four years. However, it is usually cloudy.

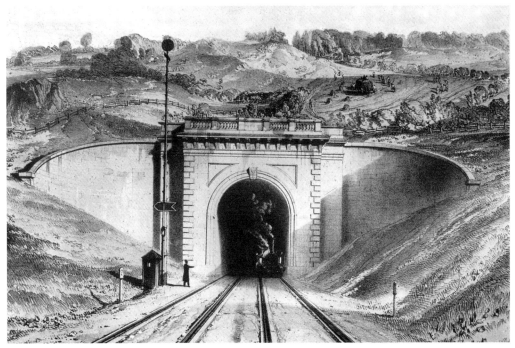

2.43   The west portal retains its original profile and has been the subject of several major restorations to maintain this important memorial to Brunel. The express is accelerating on the 1 in 100 down gradient.

2.44   Box station was provided with one of Brunel's chalets on the down side, but the footbridge was a later addition. Photographed in 1960, the station lost its passenger service in 1965. (H.C.Casserley)

2.45   East of Bath, the route had to be built through an area of fine parkland and Brunel used massive stone retaining walls to support the Kennet & Avon Canal. The view from Sydney Gardens is much the same today and the iron ballastrades appear to be the originals.   B553, C362, C966

2.46   The River Avon had to be crossed east of Bath station and this symmetrical, well ornamented stone structure was erected. It remains for posterity, being known as Dolemeads Viaduct.

2.47   The impressive station at Bath still retained its overall roof and the large goods shed to the left of it when photographed from the east in about 1895. Both appear to have been original features. Only the stonework of the station and adjacent arches remain.

2.48   Immediately to the west of Bath station, the line crossed the Avon again. Here Brunel specified a laminated timber structure and its skew configuration is seen in this downstream view, which has Old Bridge in the background. The timber bridge seen was replaced in 1878.

2.49   Bristol was Brunel's goal, but a surprising lack of vision resulted in a terminal building being erected when a national network was already envisaged. Its west elevation on Temple Gate was designed to impress Bristolians, with its turrets and castellations.   B774, C362, C966, D039, D357, D42X

2.50   The interior was equally impressive and much more so than the London terminus in the initial years of the GWR. The illustration is from about 1845 and features the hammer beam roof construction.

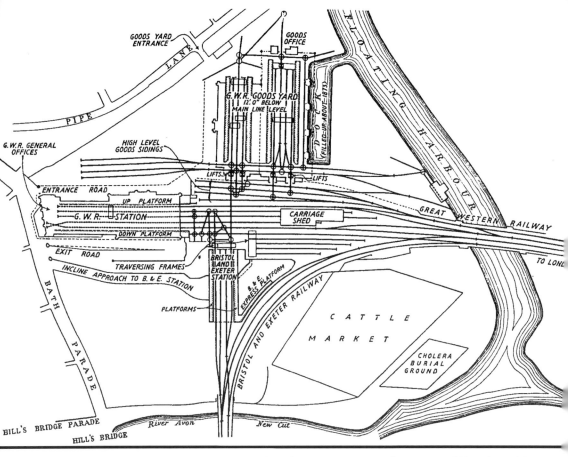

2.51   The 1845 track diagram helps to explain that the GWR's terminus was at 90° to that of the Bristol & Exeter Railway (B&ER), a legacy of the days when Bristol was considered to be the centre of the world by many. The connecting curve formed the basis of the present station.

2.52   A view east includes a train at the arrival platform and also the traverser and its winch in the foreground. The end screen is in picture 2.54.

2.53   The original goods shed is shown on the plan north of the station; its tracks were 11 feet below the running lines and wagons had to use a hydraulic lift. This was one of Brunel's more complicated schemes. The station level is apparent in the background.

2.54   This southward panorama from May 1872 seems to be from the roof of the goods shed and has the east end of Brunel's passenger shed on the right. The B&ER's office is in the background and the track to Bristol Harbour is in the foreground.

2.55   The curved part of Temple Meads was shared with the Midland Railway, which had purchased the Bristol & Gloucester Railway. It was laid to broad gauge in anticipation of a GWR buy-out, but was soon converted to standard gauge. This part of the station was for long dual gauge trains and is seen with locos of both gauges.

2.56   Brunel's passenger train shed was extended towards the camera in 1875 and is now used as a carpark. The original part is in the background of this 1956 photograph. It was last used by trains in September 1965, mainly by local services running northwards. (P.J.Kelley)

2.57   The British Empire & Commonwealth Museum was established in the original part of the terminus, its banner impinging on the south elevation. The later main entrance is in the ecclesiastical structure in the distance. The B&ER building is beyond the right border. (BE&CM)

2.58   The passenger shed was walled off at its east end and a floor provided between the platforms to form a hall for public functions or museum purposes, such as the lecture seen in progress here. (BE&CM)

2.59   The GWR's board room has been exquisitely restored by the museum. This room and the hall are both available for hire, but neither are normally open for public viewing. (BE&CM)

2.60   The *SS Great Britain* was the second of Brunel's three ships and it was returned to its birthplace in Bristol in 1970 after having been beached in the Falkland Islands in 1937. It was laid down in 1839 and floated from its dry dock in 1843, as seen. It is here that it now rests again. It followed the designer's *PS Great Western* onto the North Atlantic service and operated thereon for 20 years, before turning to the Australian run. After prolonged restoration work on the vessel, the dining room was available for functions and in 2001 a notable anniversary in railway history was celebrated here. It was 50 years earlier that the Festiniog Railway Society was formed in Bristol and three founders (including your author) were recorded alongside a full-size mural of Brunel, all bowing to their hero.

3. Bristol to the West

3.1   The B&ER office building was in good order when photographed in 2005; all evidence of its platforms had long gone. This picture is almost continuous with no. 2.57. (Author)

3.2   Seen in 2002 is Yatton up platform on which stands a Brunel-style building still containing an operational ticket office. Beyond it had been a roof that covered the Clevedon branch train and had probably been there since services started in 1847. The curved roof came from Dauntsey in 1956. (M.Turvey)   B901, D039, D187

3.3   Called Puxton & Worle since 1922, the station opened with the line as "Banwell". It carried the classic chalet on the up platform, but passengers ceased to use it in April 1964.   D039

3.4   Evidence of Brunel's styling was to be found at Highbridge. The down building (right) obscures the station for Glastonbury, which opened in 1854. A line from it to Burnham-on-Sea opened in 1858 and crossed the main line on the level at the far end of the platforms. Only bus shelters can be seen today. A681, D039

3.5   Bridgwater retains its buildings from the Brunelian era, seen here in 1934. The footbridge, canopies and goods shed were later additions; only the latter has been demolished.   D039

3.6   The exterior was recorded in 1947 when it retained most of its original features. Extensive work in 1994 created a fine ambience, details including an early type of booking office screen. Well worth visiting.   A681, D039

3.7   All trace of Brunel's work has been lost at Taunton, apart from some arches, and so a diagram of the original layout is included. Similar to that at Reading and Exeter, it shows up and down platforms separated by arrangements intended for carriage trucks, horseboxes, parcels, mail, etc.   A800, B60X, C303, C761, C826, D039

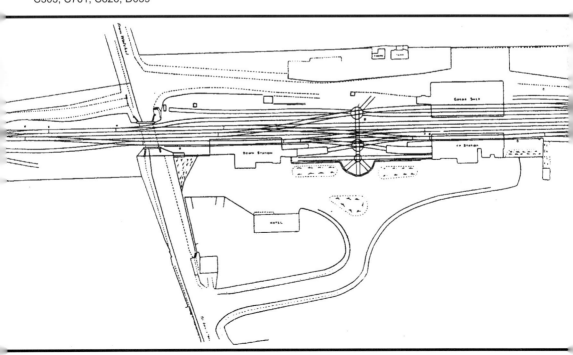

3.8   The early low-level platform at Wellington survived to appear on a postcard, but the buildings lasted only until 1931. This view is towards Taunton.   C826

3.9   Hele & Bradninch opened with the line and so it is difficult to see why the older building on the down side was non-standard. Maybe it was post-Brunel; it closed in 1964.   C826

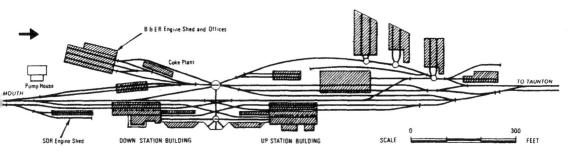

3.10   Exeter had the single-sided arrangement seen earlier at Slough, Reading and Taunton, but the operation was more complicated as the B&ER station was also used by the South Devon Railway (SDR). B154, B693, C273, C494, C621, C826

3.11   A panorama of Exeter St. Davids from the northwest features the new train shed of 1860. It includes the cathedral and the curved incline for the new extension of the London & South Western Railway (LSWR). Only parts of the original walls remain and the extent of Brunel's involvement with this building is unclear, but a pupil of his certainly was.

3.12   North of Exeter station, the goods transfer shed was built, these building being characterised by different width doors. Photographed in 1925, this historic item survived into the 21st century.

→

3.13   Adjacent to Exeter St. Davids station was the goods shed, which is thought to date from Brunel's time. It is seen on 22nd April 2000 in the company of BR 2-6-4T no. 80098 and the 10.45 Paddington to Plymouth HST. The structure was partially destroyed by fire at the north end in November 2001. (Author)

→

3.14   At the south end of the Exeter site was the first of the SDR atmospheric pump houses. After its brief life as such, it was surmounted by a massive water tank, which had just been removed when photographed in 1982. (D.H.Mitchell)

3.15   The atmospheric railway was laid as single track to Newton Abbot and this impression of it is at Exeter St. Thomas, albeit badly proportioned. The roof was replaced after the track doubling. Inexplicably, Brunel failed to extend the electric telegraph system to the engine houses and so there was a great amount of unnecessary and wasteful pumping undertaken. This fact, combined with the many other problems, gave the system a short life: 23rd February to 10th September 1848 were the dates of continuous operation, using two piston carriages.   C494

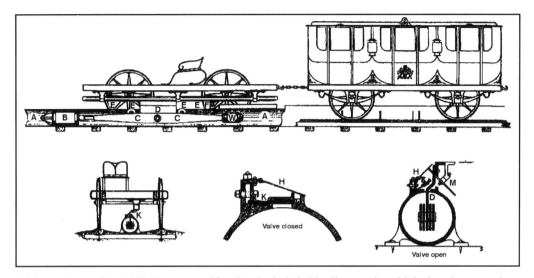

Valve closed

Valve open

3.16   Samunda's 1838 Patent specification included this diagram in which the piston carriage bodywork was omitted. These vehicles were never turned, as the connection to the piston was at an angle. At the points, there were slopes between the rails known as "piston inclines", which forced the piston up to clear the rail that it was crossing.

A.	Continuous pipe fixed between the rails	H.	Weather valve
B.	Piston	K.	Continuous airtight valve
C.	Iron plates connected to the piston	M.	Roller attached to carriage for opening
D.	Plate connecting apparatus to carriage		weather valve
E.	Metal rollers to open the continuous valve	W.	Counterweight to piston
F.	Roller attached to carriage for closing the valve		

3.17   A short length of atmospheric pipe is on display at the Didcot Railway Centre, but devoid of its continuous valve. There is also a comprehensive display of mixed gauge track, together with a goods transfer shed. (Author)

3.18 Your author, founder of Middleton Press, has built this working model of the atmospheric system, using two vacuum cleaners and a rainwater pipe. It generates publicity at shows, but Brunel was the ultimate publicist.

3.19 Nine pumping stations were used on the 20-mile route and the one at Starcross is now the most complete, albeit with its chimney top missing. A demonstration track using a 4ins diameter drain pipe was included in the museum, which opened in 1982 and closed in 1990. The building was subsequently used by the Starcross Fishing & Cruising Club.
(A.C.Mott) C494

3.20　The piston carriage is probably not correctly represented here, although the Dawlish pump house details conform with the next photograph. However, the pipe diameter on this section was only 15ins. The Italianate style of the chimneys was due to Brunel having one of his few overseas railway contracts in Italy at the time. C494

3.21　Dawlish station had a train shed and only one platform initially. The one on the right was added in May 1858. The train is about to move onto the single track to Teignmouth. The pump house was demolished in 1868 to increase siding space. The choice of the regularly-eroded seafront route has always been blamed on Brunel.

3.22   This westward view of Teignmouth has the original platform and roofs on the left. The up platform, additional roof span and covered footbridge were added in 1860. All were lost during major alterations in 1895.   C494

3.23   At Newton Abbot, a new station was built in 1861 with platforms both sides of two of the through lines. Brunel may have been consulted in its early planning, but had died before its completion.   C176, C273, C494, C605

3.24 Totnes pumping station was completed, but never used; the pipes were to have been 22ins diameter west of Newton Abbot. The Italianate chimney was demolished, but the buildings survive and were for long used as part of a dairy complex. B592, C605

3.25   The SDR accepted Brunel's chalet design for its smaller stations and this one is at Ivybridge, on the southern flank of Dartmoor. The adverse effects of the hottest sun and the heaviest snow were minimised with the projecting roof. C605

3.26   We are still at Ivybridge, but before Brunel's largely timber viaduct was replaced in 1894 by a double track structure. The station was closed in 1959, but many viaduct piers remain.

3.27   The SDR ended at a terminus at Plymouth Millbay, close to the docks. The connecting line is between the two goods sheds on the right. This is likely to be one of the last broad gauge trains to depart and the station roof was probably the final link with Brunel. It was removed in 1900.   B597, C192, C63X

3.28　　One of the most striking memorials is the Royal Albert bridge between Devon and Cornwall; each portal carries in large letters I.K.BRUNEL 1859. There was a perceived requirement for a headroom of 100ft for shipping, which gave Brunel a problem and us a joyful sight.　C63X

3.29　　One of the earliest photographs of the astonishing creation was taken from the Cornish side when the broad gauge prevailed. It lasted here until 1892. The station building dated from only 1880.

3.30   Until 1961, when a road bridge was built alongside, motorists were able to savour at leisure this great memorial as they peacefully crossed the River Tamar to Saltash.

3.31   Brunel employed four basic designs of viaduct in Cornwall. This is known as the fan-type and was employed at Moorswater, west of Liskeard. It passes over the line from Moorswater to Looe and was replaced by a parallel double track stone structure.   C222, C63X

3.32   The 1881 replacement Moorswater Viaduct was photographed in 1987, along with the remaining Cornwall Railway piers. By that time, the single line below it carried only china clay. (P.G.Barnes)

3.33   Brunel designed 22 timber viaducts for the Cornwall Railway. The final two to be in service were west of Saltash, on a section of route closed and bypassed in 1908. This is Carvedras Viaduct, on the eastern approach to Truro, and it lasted until 1902.   C672

3.34   Little trace remains of the Brunel era at the present Truro station, but the West Cornwall Railway had its own terminus south of the town at Newnham from 1855. It is seen in 1956 and is included because the WCR was a rare example of a standard gauge railway being converted to broad. The route was this gauge from 1866 to 1892 and thus a posthumous achievement for IKB.   C672, C745

3.35   West of Truro was Penwithers Viaduct, which was one of a number of Brunel's timber creations to be replaced by embankments. Work was recorded in progress in 1926.   C745

3.36   West of Redruth station was this slender viaduct which was probably photographed in the 1870s in the heyday of the local tin industry.   B308, C672

3.37   At Penzance there was a Brunel-style roof over the platforms, which lasted until 1879 when replaced by the present span. The photo is from the 1866-76 period.   C672

4. Branches South and West

4.1   The 1849 branch from Slough to Windsor passes over the River Thames north of the terminus and its bridge is seen in 1993. Although it was extensively rebuilt in 1907, many of the original girders were kept. (T.Wright)   C77X

4.2   A substantial terminal building was provided at Windsor, conveniently close to the castle. The tracks were mixed gauge here from 1862 until 1883 and the station was totally rebuilt in 1897.

4.3   The next branch south was to Hungerford and it came into use in December 1847; a branch from it to Basingstoke followed in November 1848. Mortimer was the first station on it and this northward view of it is from the 1950s. The building has been preserved, although reroofed with tiles.   B278

4.4　This westward panorama at Basingstoke has the London & South Western Railway main line on the left and the GWR train shed on the right. There was a transfer shed between the two systems, behind the camera. Dual gauge track arrived here in 1856.　A118, A185, A55X, A69X, A894, B278

4.5　The interior of the GWR station at Basingstoke featured a wheeled drawbridge between the platforms. It spanned the connection to the LSWR goods yard. The building was in use until 1932.

────▶ 4.6　Melksham was featured on a postcard in the 1900s, its down side carrying the Brunelian chalet. The station was the first on the Weymouth branch, the section to Westbury opening in 1848.　D128

────▶ 4.7　Warminster was served by a branch from Westbury from 1851 and it was a terminus until 1856, when the broad gauge was extended to Salisbury. Looking towards that place in 1928, we can see the early overall roof beyond the later footbridge. (H.C.Casserley)　B391

4.8   Salisbury was graced with an elegant structure appropriate to a cathedral city. There were probably three tracks in Brunel's day.   A673, A894, A975, B065, B391

4.9   The west elevation of Salisbury's station included a useful smoke vent. As at Basingstoke, the GWR platforms were in use until 1932.

4.10   The elegant east elevation lost its canopy, but the building is extant, although not in railway use. A footbridge (left) was provided to the LSWR's Salisbury station in 1860.

4.11   Frome was the first station south of Westbury on the Weymouth branch; its south end is seen in 1922. The main structures have lasted into the 21st century, albeit with only one track.   B774, C761

4.12   Frome train shed was recorded in 1995 after recent restoration work. The station had been bypassed in 1933 and so mostly local trains have called subsequently. (M.J.Stretton)

4.13   Another 1995 photograph completes the survey of this rare survivor of a rural station of Brunel's design, complete with train shed and still in regular use. (M.J.Stretton)

4.14   Although completed after Brunel's death, Cheddar had many of his design features. The large space between the tracks was a legacy of the broad gauge, which lasted here until 1875.   B901

4.15   A train from Yatton was recorded at Cheddar in July 1963, two months before passenger service ceased. The screen panelling is in terminal decline. (E.Wilmshurst)

4.16   Yeovil Pen Mill unusually had only one track under the roof, the up one. The structure at its far end is the footbridge, which still exists.   A762, C303, C389

4.17   The unusual Yeovil arrangement is seen from the south in the inter-war period. The curious platform layout remains in use still. The "Bulldog" is bound for Weymouth.

4.18   The Durston branch carried trains between Yeovil and Taunton. Martock was the second stop from Yeovil Town and its chalet was on the west side of the single track, but its canopies did not last until closure.   C303

4.19   The train is under Weymouth's main terminal span, the structure on the right being the goods shed. The incomplete track may be explained by gauge conversion in 1874.   A576, A657

4.20   The offices at Weymouth were still in use when photographed in 1963, but the overall roof had been cut back to the platform edges in 1951.

4.21   Clevedon's terminal building first received trains in 1847, the line branching from the B&ER at Yatton. The train shed and its canopy extension were photographed in 1963; closure followed in 1966.   D187

4.22 A single line branch to Torquay opened in 1848, but its extension to Kingswear was not completed until after Brunel's death. A branch from it to Brixham followed in 1868 and the terminus is illustrated as another posthumous example of his designs being used, although the goods shed is unique. C176

4.23 Brunel was appointed engineer to the Cornwall Railway in 1846 for construction of the Plymouth-Falmouth line. The section to Truro opened shortly before his death, but the remainder was not completed until 1863. Carnon Viaduct was on this section and was replaced in 1933. B308, C745

4.24　　Collegewood Viaduct was nearer to Falmouth, just south of Penryn station. This fine example of the fan-type viaduct survived until 1934. Penryn is in the background.　B308, C745

4.25　　Falmouth terminus was photographed in the 1920s; the roof was dismantled 30 years later, but the main building (right) survived until about 1970.　B308, C745

4.26   The entrance at Falmouth faced northwest and not the sea. Brunel specified similar designs for here and Plymouth Millbay. There is also a similarity with Weymouth.

4.27   The final West Country route to look at was known as the North Devon Railway. This is Crediton, which opened in 1851 and received an inner rail in 1862, when the LSWR leased the line. B154, B693

4.28   Services were extended to Barnstaple, which is seen in this northward panorama. Trains began running from Crediton in 1854 and were mostly standard gauge from 1863. Broad gauge freight continued to the former until 1877 and the latter until 1892.   B154, B219, B375, B60X

5. Swindon to South Wales

5.1   Pictures 2.32 to 2.36 are supplemented by two more of this operational centre of Brunel's world. This 1852 westward view has the works in the background and numerous passengers, most of whom were allegedly complaining about the refreshment arrangements.   C842, C966, D306, D462

5.2   Brunel's team designed the up side rooms for the catering contractor, who paid them, but earned the station the nickname of "Swindlem". They were bought out in 1895 and the footbridge to the down side (right) was rcmoved in 1962.

5.3   Minety & Ashton Keynes was the second station out from Swindon and it retained its chalet until closure in 1964. It was on the up side and was photographed in 1958. (H.C.Casserley)   D462

5.4   Kemble was the junction for the branch to Cirencester (right) and Brunel employed his country station features extensively here. There was no public access to the station, other than by train, until 1881, when the station was completely rebuilt.   D462

5.5   Cirencester received all trains from the south between 1841 and 1845, when services began to Gloucester, and Kemble opened. There was a roof (right) over the single platform for many years.   D462

5.6   By the 1950s, the terminus at Cirencester, by then named "Town", had become very shabby. The overall roof had long gone, as had the canopy on the north elevation. (J.Moss)

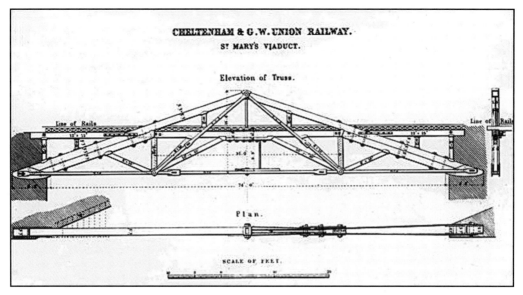

5.7   After passing through Sapperton Tunnel in the complex geology of the Cotswolds thereabouts, the line entered the Golden Valley. Gradient minimisation was a problem for Brunel in this terrain, but his viaduct over the River Frome near St. Mary's was without problem. It had six piers and lasted 27 years.

5.8   Brimscombe displayed classic Brunel styling until closure in 1964. The loco shed in the distance provided banking engines for the climb over the Cotswolds.   D462

5.9   The bay window positioning was different at Stonehouse, but they were still a complementary pair of buildings. Bureaucratic bungling in the 1970s unfortunately brought about their demise and Brunel to probably turn in his grave at Kensal Green.   D462

5.10   Nothing of note remains of Brunel's work at Gloucester or Cheltenham and so we run eight miles beyond the former to the junction of the South Wales line with the 1855 Hereford route. It is seen in about 1900, after two extra platforms had been added on the left, for the branch trains.   D667

5.11   Lydney was photographed in about 1923, but no trace of Brunel's creation now remains, although a similar building presently stands on the down platform, right.   D667

5.12   The major obstacle for those entering South Wales was the deep valley of the River Wye. This southward view gives a good impression of the landscape and the massive embankment which Brunel built in Chepstow to reach his unique bridge.   D667

5.13   The unique and distinctive structure is seen from the other side, with the sheer limestone cliffs of the east bank on the right. No scaffolding was used, as Brunel engaged unemployed mariners experienced with ropes on sailing ships. The cast iron columns remain, but the trusses were dismantled in 1962.

5.14   Chepstow was a terminus for trains from Swansea for 15 months, until the bridge was opened in September 1851. This impression is thought to date from that period and was made from south of the station.   D667

5.15   The north elevation was recorded in 1982; both buildings had been jacked up 22 inches in 1877-78, as Brunel's platforms were deemed to be too low by that time. They are now listed buildings. (D.Thompson)

5.16   The next major river crossing was that of the Usk at Newport. Here Brunel provided one of his timber structures, but part of it was destroyed by fire before the opening. One span was replaced by wrought iron and the others followed in 1886, but the present bridge dates from 1924.   D160, D306, D543, D667

5.17   This westward panorama of Newport is probably as Brunel created it, with engine shed straight ahead, the goods shed on the left and the carriage sheds on the right. The broad gauge tracks disappeared in 1872.

5.18   A November 2005 view in the same direction has the only remaining Brunelian buildings on the right; they had for long had a fresh use as goods sheds. The EWS locomotives on the left stand close to the site of the original engine shed. (Author)

5.19   Brunel made a major change to Welsh scenery when he built this fine structure over the River Tawe, a mile or so north of Swansea. He had been engineer to the South Wales Railway since 1844 and the 37 spans of Landore Viaduct carried trains from 1850 until the 1880s.

5.20   The centre span of Landore Viaduct was 110ft in length and was ingeniously composed of an arch within an arch. It was entirely of timber construction. Other relics of Brunel's activities in South Wales are few and of no great significance.

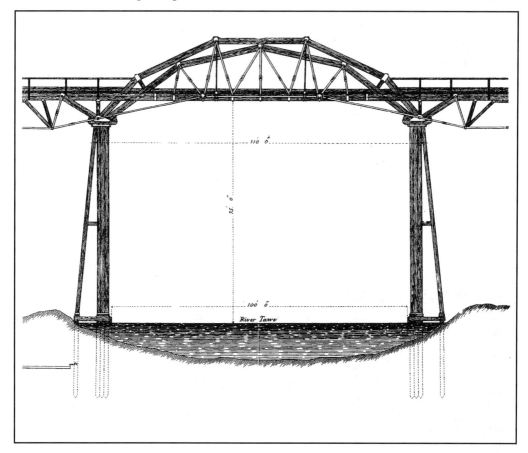

Brunel and Standard Gauge

5.21   Brunel was inconsistent and did not suggest broad gauge for the Taff Vale Railway between Cardiff and Merthyr Tydfil. It opened with standard gauge track in 1840, at a time when the Festiniog Railway was demonstrating to the world the practicality of two-foot gauge for mineral railways in hilly terrain. Pontypridd station is seen before rebuilding in 1891; it is a rare glimpse of a conventional platform spacing with Brunelian structures.

5.22   North of the station is Newbridge Viaduct, the nearest span being designed by Brunel. The smaller arches were added for a second track in 1862. The route is sharply curved and steeply graded, parts having been rope worked before Brunel's arrival.

5.23   Goitre Coed Viaduct still carries trains between Cardiff and Merthyr although much widened. Brunel specified slender octagonal masonry columns, a mere 14ft between flats. This illustration was produced in 1845 and shows a train northbound. Trevithick's 1804 tramway had passed under it carrying much coal and iron to the Glamorganshire Canal. Items for Brunel's other projects would have gone this way until the railway was completed.

6. Northwards from Didcot

6.1 The Didcot Railway Centre is the leader in the presentation of broad gauge exhibits. Not only has the original Didcot transfer shed been rebuilt on the site, but there is much dual gauge track. A new high was reached in 2005 with the steaming of the replica of the 1840 *Fire Fly* right. Brunel retired from locomotive design at an early age. (M.J.Stretton) C133, C796, C842, D020

6.2 Trains still called at Culham, but the up side building was unused when photographed in 1990. A new platform was soon built further north and a major renovation scheme was completed in 2005. It forms a fine rural memorial to Brunel. (P.G.Barnes) D020

6.3   The short branch to Abingdon opened in 1856 and was converted to standard gauge in 1872. The building was replaced in 1908, following a major shunting accident. This is a "Leo" class 0-6-0T. The extent of Brunel's involvement is not certain. D020

6.4   No trace of Brunel's era is visible at Oxford and so we move north to Heyford, where this fine example of his work was in use until staffing ceased in the 1960s. Demolition by the unappreciative followed. Please see 7.1 and 7.2 for early views of Oxford.   D020

6.5   Also on the west side was the main building at Aynho, but trains ceased to call here in 1964. However, it was still standing at the end of that century, albeit in a decrepit state.   D020

6.6   Banbury was provided with a substantial train shed, which is seen from the south in 1950, by which time it was in poor condition and the short down platform was an increasing handicap.   C850, D020, D276, D578

6.7   The west elevation at Banbury was recorded in 1953 and was similar to some of the entrances seen earlier. Rebuilding took place in 1957 and all historic items were lost. (C.B.Swallow)

6.8   A southward view of Banbury in 1932 includes platforms added after Brunel's time and the multitude of chimneys that he had to specify on all his works, but were seldom so tall.

6.9   About 15 miles north was Southam Road & Harbury station. A postcard reveals the familiar chalet features, albeit unusually obscured. The B4451 bridge is in the background in this southward view of another station which lost its passenger service in 1964.   D276

6.10   Dorridge had a chalet-style building with the roundhead windows employed at other locations. Many changes took place during the quadrupling of this part of the route in 1933 and little remains of the earlier era.   D276

6.11   Solihull was provided with two buildings of the best Brunelian style, but both were lost in 1933, as was the footbridge. This is the view towards Birmingham.   D276

6.12   Although Acocks Green opened with the route, it had little more than garden sheds. The up side building (right) was replicated at Hatton, although that was a junction for Stratford-upon-Avon. Reminders of Brunel further north are not notable, despite his activity in Wolverhampton.   D276

7. Oxford Westwards

7.1   The terminus at Oxford of the branch from Didcot was south of the city, the line ending on the bank of the River Isis at Grandpont. It was not used by passengers after 1852, but broad gauge freight traffic continued until 1872.   A525, D020, D055, D152, D578

7.2   The present through station at Oxford came into use in 1852, although trains ran north to Banbury from 1850. Its overall roof was seldom photographed, as it was demolished in 1890. It appears in the 1875 flood pictures; part of the London & North Western Railway's terminus is on the right. The GWR station approach is on the left.

7.3   Charlbury is seen in 1969, but this up side building was still in good condition and staffed, at least on workday mornings, at the start of the 21st century. A local group was active in its conservation. (J.E.Norris/KRM) D152

7.4   In the absence of firm evidence of links with Brunel's buildings in the Midlands, we will end our tour with a little known incident which must have been indelible in his mind.

The Battle of Mickleton

The Oxford Worcester and Wolverhampton Railway (OWWR) was closely associated during its formative years with the GWR, but relations turned sour prior to the protracted construction period. Sir Morton Peto was a key figure in the main contracting firm and by July 1851 a Mr. Marchant was the only partner remaining in the firm of sub-contractors building Campden Tunnel, very slowly. The delays were largely due to lethargic payments by the cash-starved OWWR.

Peto decided to take over the site and Marchant's equipment by force, but was unsuccessful. The OWWR's engineer, I.K.Brunel, arrived with about 300 men on Friday 20th July 1851 to find around 100 of Marchant's workers well armed and the county magistrate in attendance. He advised Brunel not to fight and to leave the site. Next day, Brunel returned with his gang, assuming that the magistrate would not be present on a Saturday. However, he had returned with a large number of policemen carrying cutlasses and had read the Riot Act to Marchant's force and proceeded to do the same to Brunel's. The latter withdrew. Brunel broke the Sabbath by ordering gangs to travel from other construction sites. At around 3am on Monday morning he advanced with a total of over 500 navvies and overwhelmed Marchant, despite his pistol. Ugly encounters continued and estimates put Brunel's manpower eventually at 2000. Fighting continued until about 4pm, by which time the police were supported by the Gloucestershire Artillery. Marchant lost his contract and equipment, Peto lost his reputation and Brunel lost his patience, resigning as engineer to the OWWR in March 1852. Mickleton became a name carved in railway history, but it was not used subsequently, (except for a halt briefly); the tunnel was named after nearby Campden.

MP Middleton Press

EVOLVING THE ULTIMATE RAIL ENCYCLOPEDIA

Easebourne Lane, Midhurst, West Sussex.
GU29 9AZ   Tel:01730 813169
www.middletonpress.co.uk   email:info@middletonpress.co.uk

A-0 906520   B-1 873793   C-1 901706   D-1 904474

OOP Out of Print at time of printing - Please check current availability   **BROCHURE AVAILABLE SHOWING NEW TITLES**